Created and published by Em & Friends
Distributed by Knock Knock LLC
6695 Green Valley Circle, #5167
Culver City, CA 90230
emandfriends.com

Em & Friends is a trademark of Knock Knock LLC

ISBN: 978-164246-482-5
UPC: 812729029596

10 9 8 7 6 5 4 3 2 1

Happyish

by **NORA McINERNY**

Hi you,

This is not a gratitude journal. You might find gratitude within it, but only if you want to. There are no secrets, tips, or tricks in this journal, no road map to becoming the most Optimal You or to Living the Life of Your Dreams.

No. This journal is here to help you document who and how you are on a daily basis, to create a record of the life you have right now, no pressure and no rules (okay, there are a few rules, but they're good for you, I promise).

I've called it Happyish because I'm a recovering perfectionist who spent years freeing herself from the chokehold of the self-help industry and all its promises: that life can be solved, fixed, tamed. It cannot, but I didn't know that until my life fell apart.

If that sounds dramatic, it's because it was dramatic. In 2014, I lost my second pregnancy at 11 weeks and 6 days. Five days later, my father died of cancer. Six weeks after that, my husband Aaron died of the brain cancer he'd been living with for three years. Immediately, the Optimist Industrial Complex whirred to life around me: everyone wanted me to be better, and fast.

And I tried, really. I went to the gym and I put on lipstick and I smiled like everything was fine when really, I was as unwell as I'd ever been. But of course I was!

I was having a normal, natural reaction to loss! It was actually perfectly fine that I wasn't fine, but the more I tried to pretend I was okay, the more terrible I felt.

Now, I have nothing against positivity, and I'm generally a pretty upbeat person. But Toxic Positivity insists that we *only* look at the bright side, that we focus on the silver lining even when the storm clouds are turning into a hurricane around us. It's unhelpful and unhealthy... and it doesn't work; studies have shown that the pursuit of happiness can actually make you less happy. So does that mean we're all just destined to be miserable forever? Of course not. Because things are hardly ever just miserable. If you've ever laughed at a funeral or cried at a wedding, you know that we're capable of experiencing a whole lot of feelings seemingly all at once.

The self-improvement space is a multibillion-dollar industry that thrives on our human desire for *more*: more success, more mastery, more happiness. It tells us how to optimize our lives and live up to our potential, how to hack our way out of who and where we are with countless tips and tricks that *could* work if only life were that simple.

But there were no tips and tricks that could bring back my father or my husband or that baby, no secret to restoring the family and the life that I'd dreamed of. I knew I wouldn't always feel like this, but I *did* feel like this.

I didn't need to deny it, I needed to document it.

I'd always been a journaler, but a big, blank page was too much for me to confront every day. Grief had eradicated my ability to manage daily tasks, and I needed a way to keep track of what I was doing to take care of myself. With a blank notebook and a ruler left over from middle school math class, I made my own version of the journal you're holding today.

Every day, I took a few moments to think about *how* I was doing and *what* I was doing. There were no big assignments, and no pressure, and even in my addled state, I could spend a couple moments on the page. Day by by, patterns emerged. I could see not just my grief and sorrow, but the joy and gratitude that existed side-by-side even in those dark days.

I wasn't happy like I'd been before, but I was happyish, and that was more than good enough for me.

Years later, I still practice this same kind of journaling not as a way to fix myself, but as a way to stay present in my life... even when it's hard.

Whether you're starting this journal in your worst days, your best days or your... okayest days, I can promise you these things:

* This journal is *not* going to change your life. It is going to catalog your life in all of its messy and magnificent glory, and give you a low-stress way to stay present with yourself and your life.

* Using this journal will not help you become your Best Self, it will help you witness yourself and your life.

* There are no secrets within these pages, other than the ones you discover yourself.

Ready? Let's go.

Nora

HOW THIS JOURNAL WORKS
(AKA INSTRUCTIONS)

First things first, a few rules:

LOWER YOUR EXPECTATIONS. We aren't here to life-hack or growth-hack or any-kind-of-hack. We aren't here to optimize or synergize. We are going to unsubscribe from the thought patterns that have encouraged us to live our "best life" and instead just live "a life." We are not seeking unbridled happiness but its more stable cousin, a state of happy*ish*.

DON'T SHOULD YOURSELF. Should is a comparison, and when has comparison ever made something better? You might be tempted to compare where you are to where you *thought* you'd be "if only"... nope! We're not wasting our time on *should*, not in this journal.

BE HONEST. The only person who will see this journal is you and Future You. There's no need to slap on your rose-colored glasses or to downplay your joys and wins. It all matters. It all counts.

OKAY, LET'S GET STARTED...

Day by day, you'll keep track of the things that contribute to your own personal happyish-ness. You'll notice we aren't tracking our goals... and that's on purpose. Because what you accomplish is not as important as who and how you are.

what are you feeling?

We know, we know, it changes by the minute. Take some time before you start the journal to think about the feelings and sensations you commonly experience. We'll track them moving forward. I track: anger, anxiety, depression, and overall energy. What do you want to monitor?

- ....
- ....
- ....
- ....
- ....

what makes you feel good?

- ....
- ....
- ....
- ....
- ....

Think small (really small, even). What are the things you can do that reliably make your days better? There are no wrong answers except for the clearly self-destructive one that you know doesn't actually work. For me, these things are connection (calling a friend or family member), sleep (8 hours!), movement (exercise feels like a punishment), and reading.

HERE'S HOW A FILLED-OUT DAY MIGHT LOOK...

On a scale of 1–10, how did these feelings/sensations show up today?

Week Of: December 5th

TUESDAY in a sentence: Got an unexpected phone call from an old friend—decided to meet up for dinner

What's good about my life: My dog thinks I'm the best.

What I did well today: I was patient with a rude customer.

Blah: Annoying call from my boss—ughhh.

MOODS

3	4	4	8
Anger	Anxiety	Depression	Energy

HABITS

✓		✓	
Connection	Sleep	Movement	Reading

I don't care how small these things are! The point is to give yourself some credit.

These are either done (you met your own personal definition for completion), or they aren't. No big deal either way, we're just keeping track!

You've also got space every week and once a month to reflect on the days that have passed and see your life for yourself: what you did well, what bugged you, your wins and losses. You don't need to ruminate or obsess over stuff. The main idea is just to process things and keep moving in whatever best-ish, happyish ways you can—week by week, month by month.

HERE'S HOW A WEEK IN REVIEW MIGHT LOOK...

Week In Review: December 5th

YA WIN SOME, YA LOSE SOME
The best & worst of last week

YAY!

Took 5 walks

Lunch with my niece

BOO!

Lost my headphones

Picked a fight with my partner for no reason

RATE THIS WEEK'S OVERALL HAPPYISHNESS:

UN-HAPPYISH   HAPPYISH

A brief weekly review gives you space to reflect on the past week.

LIFE IS TOUGH. SO ARE YOU.

That said, you're perfectly welcome to be as soft as you need to be at any time. You can be a feather bed. A bowl of jelly. A cloud wrapped in cotton candy.

Week Of:

MONDAY in a sentence: ....

....

What's good about my life: ....

....

What I did well today: ....

....

Blah: ....

MOODS ○ ○ ○ ○

HABITS ○ ○ ○ ○

TUESDAY in a sentence: ....

....

What's good about my life: ....

....

What I did well today: ....

....

Blah: ....

MOODS ○ ○ ○ ○

HABITS ○ ○ ○ ○

WEDNESDAY in a sentence: ....

....

What's good about my life: ....

....

What I did well today: ....

....

Blah: ....

MOODS ○ ○ ○ ○

HABITS ○ ○ ○ ○

THURSDAY in a sentence: ....

....

What's good about my life: ....

....

What I did well today: ....

....

Blah: ....

MOODS ○ ○ ○ ○

HABITS ○ ○ ○ ○

FRIDAY in a sentence: ....

....

What's good about my life: ....

....

What I did well today: ....

....

Blah: ....

....

MOODS ○ ○ ○ ○

HABITS ○ ○ ○ ○

SATURDAY in a sentence: ....

....

What's good about my life: ....

....

What I did well today: ....

....

Blah: ....

....

MOODS ○ ○ ○ ○

HABITS ○ ○ ○ ○

SUNDAY in a sentence: ....

....

What's good about my life: ....

....

What I did well today: ....

....

Blah: ....

....

MOODS ○ ○ ○ ○

HABITS ○ ○ ○ ○

Week In Review: ....

YA WIN SOME, YA LOSE SOME
The best & worst of this week

YAY!   BOO!

RATE THIS WEEK'S
OVERALL HAPPYISHNESS:

UN-HAPPYISH   HAPPYISH

Week Of:

MONDAY in a sentence:

What's good about my life:

What I did well today:

Blah:

MOODS

HABITS

TUESDAY in a sentence:

What's good about my life:

What I did well today:

Blah:

MOODS

HABITS

WEDNESDAY in a sentence:

What's good about my life:

What I did well today:

Blah:

MOODS

HABITS

THURSDAY in a sentence:

What's good about my life:

What I did well today:

Blah:

MOODS

HABITS

FRIDAY in a sentence: ....

....

What's good about my life: ....

.... MOODS

What I did well today: ....

Blah: .... HABITS

....

SATURDAY in a sentence: ....

....

What's good about my life: .... MOODS

....

What I did well today: ....

.... HABITS

Blah: ....

....

SUNDAY in a sentence: ....

....

What's good about my life: .... MOODS

....

What I did well today: ....

.... HABITS

Blah: ....

....

Week In Review: ....

YA WIN SOME, YA LOSE SOME
The best & worst of this week

YAY!

BOO!

RATE THIS WEEK'S
OVERALL HAPPYISHNESS:

UN-HAPPYISH   HAPPYISH

Week Of:

MONDAY in a sentence:..

....

What's good about my life:..

What I did well today:..

Blah:..

MOODS

HABITS

TUESDAY in a sentence:..

What's good about my life:..

What I did well today:..

Blah:..

MOODS

HABITS

WEDNESDAY in a sentence:..

What's good about my life:..

What I did well today:..

Blah:..

MOODS

HABITS

THURSDAY in a sentence:..

What's good about my life:..

What I did well today:..

Blah:..

MOODS

HABITS

FRIDAY in a sentence: ....

....

What's good about my life: ....

....

What I did well today: ....

....

Blah: ....

....

MOODS

HABITS

SATURDAY in a sentence: ....

....

What's good about my life: ....

....

What I did well today: ....

....

Blah: ....

....

MOODS

HABITS

SUNDAY in a sentence: ....

....

What's good about my life: ....

....

What I did well today: ....

....

Blah: ....

....

MOODS

HABITS

Week In Review: ....

YA WIN SOME, YA LOSE SOME
The best & worst of this week

**RATE THIS WEEK'S
OVERALL HAPPYISHNESS:**

YAY!

BOO!

UN-HAPPYISH   HAPPYISH

Week Of:

MONDAY in a sentence:..

....

What's good about my life: ....

....

What I did well today: ....

....

Blah: ....

....

MOODS

HABITS

TUESDAY in a sentence:...

....

What's good about my life: ....

....

What I did well today: ....

....

Blah: ....

....

MOODS

HABITS

WEDNESDAY in a sentence: ....

....

What's good about my life: ....

....

What I did well today: ....

....

Blah: ....

....

MOODS

HABITS

THURSDAY in a sentence: ....

....

What's good about my life: ....

....

What I did well today: ....

....

Blah: ....

....

MOODS

HABITS

FRIDAY in a sentence: ....

....

What's good about my life: ....

....

What I did well today: ....

....

Blah: ....

....

MOODS

HABITS

SATURDAY in a sentence: ....

....

What's good about my life: ....

....

What I did well today: ....

....

Blah: ....

....

MOODS

HABITS

SUNDAY in a sentence: ....

....

What's good about my life: ....

....

What I did well today: ....

....

Blah: ....

....

MOODS

HABITS

Week In Review: ....

YA WIN SOME, YA LOSE SOME
The best & worst of this week

YAY!

BOO!

RATE THIS WEEK'S
OVERALL HAPPYISHNESS:

UN-HAPPYISH

HAPPYISH

QUIT LIST: What are the things/people/actions/thoughts you can quit this month: the weekly yoga class you dread? The coffee shop with the rude baristas? Your morning doomscroll? These are tangible changes you can make... but you don't have to!

I quit... ....

....

....

....

....

BRAGGABLE: Please save your humble pie for another occasion. This is a space to tell yourself everything you did well this month. Like, everything. You flossed once? You didn't roll your eyes at your annoying neighbor? You told your partner exactly why you were angry instead of making them guess? WELL DONE!

I feel great about... ....

....

....

....

....

LET IT BURN: Let's not pretend that everything is perfect or fine or just dandy. Here's a space for you to write down all your icky stuff: the jealous feelings that make you feel gross, the negative things you say to yourself, the texts you wanted to send but didn't, because you knew it was totally inappropriate. Write it down. Tear it out. Burn it up. Or just fold the page over. The point is... these are the things you can let go.

I acknowledge & let go of... ....

....

....

....

WE MAKE IT UP AS WE GO,

and sometimes we are big and generous and sometimes we are small and petty. We say the wrong things, we obsess over all the ways we got it wrong and all the ways that other people did, too. The only thing I know for sure is that it is okay not to know everything, to try and fail and to sometimes suck at life, as long as you try to get better.

Week Of:

MONDAY in a sentence: ....

....

What's good about my life: ....

....

What I did well today: ....

....

Blah: ....

....

MOODS

HABITS

TUESDAY in a sentence: ....

What's good about my life: ....

....

What I did well today: ....

....

Blah: ....

....

MOODS

HABITS

WEDNESDAY in a sentence: ....

....

What's good about my life: ....

....

What I did well today: ....

....

Blah: ....

....

MOODS

HABITS

THURSDAY in a sentence: ....

....

What's good about my life: ....

....

What I did well today: ....

....

Blah: ....

....

MOODS

HABITS

FRIDAY in a sentence: ....

.... MOODS

What's good about my life: ....

....

What I did well today: ....

.... HABITS

Blah: ....

....

SATURDAY in a sentence: ....

.... MOODS

What's good about my life: ....

....

What I did well today: ....

.... HABITS

Blah: ....

....

SUNDAY in a sentence: ....

.... MOODS

What's good about my life: ....

....

What I did well today: ....

.... HABITS

Blah: ....

....

Week In Review:

YA WIN SOME, YA LOSE SOME
The best & worst of this week

YAY!

BOO!

RATE THIS WEEK'S OVERALL HAPPYISHNESS:

UN-HAPPYISH   HAPPYISH

Week Of:

MONDAY in a sentence:

What's good about my life:

What I did well today:

Blah:

MOODS

HABITS

TUESDAY in a sentence:

What's good about my life:

What I did well today:

Blah:

MOODS

HABITS

WEDNESDAY in a sentence:

What's good about my life:

What I did well today:

Blah:

MOODS

HABITS

THURSDAY in a sentence:

What's good about my life:

What I did well today:

Blah:

MOODS

HABITS

FRIDAY in a sentence: ....

....

What's good about my life: ....

....

What I did well today: ....

....

Blah: ....

....

MOODS

HABITS

SATURDAY in a sentence: ....

....

What's good about my life: ....

....

What I did well today: ....

....

Blah: ....

....

MOODS

HABITS

SUNDAY in a sentence: ....

....

What's good about my life: ....

....

What I did well today: ....

....

Blah: ....

....

MOODS

HABITS

Week In Review: ....

YA WIN SOME, YA LOSE SOME
The best & worst of this week

YAY!

BOO!

**RATE THIS WEEK'S
OVERALL HAPPYISHNESS:**

UN-HAPPYISH   HAPPYISH

Week Of: ....

MONDAY in a sentence: ....

....

What's good about my life: ....

....

What I did well today: ....

....

Blah: ....

....

TUESDAY in a sentence: ....

What's good about my life: ....

....

What I did well today: ....

....

Blah: ....

....

WEDNESDAY in a sentence: ....

....

What's good about my life: ....

....

What I did well today: ....

....

Blah: ....

....

THURSDAY in a sentence: ....

....

What's good about my life: ....

....

What I did well today: ....

....

Blah: ....

....

FRIDAY in a sentence: ....

....

What's good about my life: .... ◯ ◯ ◯ ◯ **MOODS**

What I did well today: ....

Blah: .... ◯ ◯ ◯ ◯ **HABITS**

....

SATURDAY in a sentence: ....

....

What's good about my life: .... ◯ ◯ ◯ ◯ **MOODS**

What I did well today: ....

Blah: .... ◯ ◯ ◯ ◯ **HABITS**

....

SUNDAY in a sentence: ....

....

What's good about my life: .... ◯ ◯ ◯ ◯ **MOODS**

What I did well today: ....

Blah: .... ◯ ◯ ◯ ◯ **HABITS**

....

Week In Review: ....

YA WIN SOME, YA LOSE SOME
The best & worst of this week

RATE THIS WEEK'S
OVERALL HAPPYISHNESS:

YAY!   BOO!

UN-HAPPYISH   HAPPYISH

Week Of: ....

MONDAY in a sentence: ....

....   ◯ ◯ ◯ ◯   **MOODS**

What's good about my life: ....

....   ◯ ◯ ◯ ◯   **HABITS**

What I did well today: ....

Blah: ....

TUESDAY in a sentence: ....

....   ◯ ◯ ◯ ◯   **MOODS**

What's good about my life: ....

What I did well today: ....   ◯ ◯ ◯ ◯   **HABITS**

Blah: ....

WEDNESDAY in a sentence: ....

....   ◯ ◯ ◯ ◯   **MOODS**

What's good about my life: ....

What I did well today: ....

....   ◯ ◯ ◯ ◯   **HABITS**

Blah: ....

THURSDAY in a sentence: ....

....   ◯ ◯ ◯ ◯   **MOODS**

What's good about my life: ....

What I did well today: ....

....   ◯ ◯ ◯ ◯   **HABITS**

Blah: ....

FRIDAY in a sentence: ....

....

What's good about my life: ....

....

What I did well today: ....

....

Blah: ....

....

MOODS

HABITS

SATURDAY in a sentence: ....

....

What's good about my life: ....

....

What I did well today: ....

....

Blah: ....

....

MOODS

HABITS

SUNDAY in a sentence: ....

....

What's good about my life: ....

....

What I did well today: ....

....

Blah: ....

....

MOODS

HABITS

Week In Review: ....

YA WIN SOME, YA LOSE SOME
The best & worst of this week

RATE THIS WEEK'S
OVERALL HAPPYISHNESS:

YAY!

BOO!

UN-HAPPYISH   HAPPYISH

QUIT LIST: What are the things/people/actions/thoughts you can quit this month: the weekly yoga class you dread? The coffee shop with the rude baristas? Your morning doomscroll? These are tangible changes you can make... but you don't have to!

I quit... ....
....
....
....
....

BRAGGABLE: Please save your humble pie for another occasion. This is a space to tell yourself everything you did well this month. Like, everything. You flossed once? You didn't roll your eyes at your annoying neighbor? You told your partner exactly why you were angry instead of making them guess? WELL DONE!

I feel great about... ....
....
....
....
....

LET IT BURN: Let's not pretend that everything is perfect or fine or just dandy. Here's a space for you to write down all your icky stuff: the jealous feelings that make you feel gross, the negative things you say to yourself, the texts you wanted to send but didn't, because you knew it was totally inappropriate. Write it down. Tear it out. Burn it up. Or just fold the page over. The point is... these are the things you can let go.

I acknowledge & let go of... ....
....
....
....
....

THE WORLD WILL KEEP SPINNING,

and your life will get a little bit better every time you give up on the sh*t that is taking you away from your one wild and precious life.

Week Of:

MONDAY in a sentence:

What's good about my life:

What I did well today:

Blah:

MOODS ○ ○ ○ ○

HABITS ○ ○ ○ ○

TUESDAY in a sentence:

What's good about my life:

What I did well today:

Blah:

MOODS ○ ○ ○ ○

HABITS ○ ○ ○ ○

WEDNESDAY in a sentence:

What's good about my life:

What I did well today:

Blah:

MOODS ○ ○ ○ ○

HABITS ○ ○ ○ ○

THURSDAY in a sentence:

What's good about my life:

What I did well today:

Blah:

MOODS ○ ○ ○ ○

HABITS ○ ○ ○ ○

FRIDAY in a sentence: ....

....

What's good about my life: ....

....

MOODS

What I did well today: ....

....

Blah: ....

....

HABITS

SATURDAY in a sentence: ....

....

What's good about my life: ....

....

MOODS

What I did well today: ....

....

Blah: ....

....

HABITS

SUNDAY in a sentence: ....

....

What's good about my life: ....

....

MOODS

What I did well today: ....

....

Blah: ....

....

HABITS

Week In Review: ....

YA WIN SOME, YA LOSE SOME
The best & worst of this week

RATE THIS WEEK'S
OVERALL HAPPYISHNESS:

YAY!

BOO!

UN-HAPPYISH   HAPPYISH

Week Of: ....

MONDAY in a sentence: ....

....

What's good about my life: ....

....

What I did well today: ....

....

Blah: ....

....

MOODS

HABITS

TUESDAY in a sentence: ....

....

What's good about my life: ....

....

What I did well today: ....

....

Blah: ....

....

MOODS

HABITS

WEDNESDAY in a sentence: ....

....

What's good about my life: ....

....

What I did well today: ....

....

Blah: ....

....

MOODS

HABITS

THURSDAY in a sentence: ....

....

What's good about my life: ....

....

What I did well today: ....

....

Blah: ....

....

MOODS

HABITS

FRIDAY in a sentence: ....

What's good about my life: ....

MOODS

What I did well today: ....

HABITS

Blah: ....

SATURDAY in a sentence: ....

What's good about my life: ....

MOODS

What I did well today: ....

HABITS

Blah: ....

SUNDAY in a sentence: ....

What's good about my life: ....

MOODS

What I did well today: ....

HABITS

Blah: ....

Week In Review: ....

YA WIN SOME, YA LOSE SOME
The best & worst of this week

**RATE THIS WEEK'S
OVERALL HAPPYISHNESS:**

YAY!   BOO!

UN-HAPPYISH   HAPPYISH

Week Of:

MONDAY in a sentence:

What's good about my life:

What I did well today:

Blah:

MOODS

HABITS

TUESDAY in a sentence:

What's good about my life:

What I did well today:

Blah:

MOODS

HABITS

WEDNESDAY in a sentence:

What's good about my life:

What I did well today:

Blah:

MOODS

HABITS

THURSDAY in a sentence:

What's good about my life:

What I did well today:

Blah:

MOODS

HABITS

FRIDAY in a sentence: ....

....

What's good about my life: ....

....

What I did well today: ....

....

Blah: ....

....

MOODS

HABITS

SATURDAY in a sentence: ....

....

What's good about my life: ....

....

What I did well today: ....

....

Blah: ....

....

MOODS

HABITS

SUNDAY in a sentence: ....

....

What's good about my life: ....

....

What I did well today: ....

....

Blah: ....

....

MOODS

HABITS

Week In Review: ....

YA WIN SOME, YA LOSE SOME
The best & worst of this week

YAY!

BOO!

RATE THIS WEEK'S
OVERALL HAPPYISHNESS:

UN-HAPPYISH   HAPPYISH

Week Of:

MONDAY in a sentence: ....
....

What's good about my life: ....
....

What I did well today: ....
....

Blah: ....
....

MOODS ○ ○ ○ ○

HABITS ○ ○ ○ ○

TUESDAY in a sentence: ....
....

What's good about my life: ....
....

What I did well today: ....
....

Blah: ....
....

MOODS ○ ○ ○ ○

HABITS ○ ○ ○ ○

WEDNESDAY in a sentence: ....
....

What's good about my life: ....
....

What I did well today: ....
....

Blah: ....
....

MOODS ○ ○ ○ ○

HABITS ○ ○ ○ ○

THURSDAY in a sentence: ....
....

What's good about my life: ....
....

What I did well today: ....
....

Blah: ....
....

MOODS ○ ○ ○ ○

HABITS ○ ○ ○ ○

FRIDAY in a sentence: ....

What's good about my life: ....

What I did well today: ....

Blah: ....

MOODS

HABITS

SATURDAY in a sentence: ....

What's good about my life: ....

What I did well today: ....

Blah: ....

MOODS

HABITS

SUNDAY in a sentence: ....

What's good about my life: ....

What I did well today: ....

Blah: ....

MOODS

HABITS

Week In Review: ....

YA WIN SOME, YA LOSE SOME
The best & worst of this week

YAY!

BOO!

RATE THIS WEEK'S
OVERALL HAPPYISHNESS:

UN-HAPPYISH   HAPPYISH

Month In Review:

QUIT LIST: What are the things/people/actions/thoughts you can quit this month: the weekly yoga class you dread? The coffee shop with the rude baristas? Your morning doomscroll? These are tangible changes you can make... but you don't have to!

I quit... ....

....

....

....

....

BRAGGABLE: Please save your humble pie for another occasion. This is a space to tell yourself everything you did well this month. Like, everything. You flossed once? You didn't roll your eyes at your annoying neighbor? You told your partner exactly why you were angry instead of making them guess? WELL DONE!

I feel great about... ....

....

....

....

....

LET IT BURN: Let's not pretend that everything is perfect or fine or just dandy. Here's a space for you to write down all your icky stuff: the jealous feelings that make you feel gross, the negative things you say to yourself, the texts you wanted to send but didn't, because you knew it was totally inappropriate. Write it down. Tear it out. Burn it up. Or just fold the page over. The point is... these are the things you can let go.

I acknowledge & let go of... ....

....

....

....

....

NO MATTER HOW MANY LEMONS LIFE GIVES YOU, YOU DON'T OWE ANYONE A GLASS OF LEMONADE.

Week Of:

MONDAY in a sentence:...

....

What's good about my life: ....

....

What I did well today: ....

....

Blah: ....

....

MOODS ⚪ ⚪ ⚪ ⚪

HABITS ⚪ ⚪ ⚪ ⚪

TUESDAY in a sentence:...

....

What's good about my life: ....

....

What I did well today: ....

....

Blah: ....

....

MOODS ⚪ ⚪ ⚪ ⚪

HABITS ⚪ ⚪ ⚪ ⚪

WEDNESDAY in a sentence:...

....

What's good about my life: ....

....

What I did well today: ....

....

Blah: ....

....

MOODS ⚪ ⚪ ⚪ ⚪

HABITS ⚪ ⚪ ⚪ ⚪

THURSDAY in a sentence:...

....

What's good about my life: ....

....

What I did well today: ....

....

Blah: ....

....

MOODS ⚪ ⚪ ⚪ ⚪

HABITS ⚪ ⚪ ⚪ ⚪

FRIDAY in a sentence: ....

....

What's good about my life: ....

....

What I did well today: ....

....

Blah: ....

....

MOODS

HABITS

SATURDAY in a sentence: ....

....

What's good about my life: ....

....

What I did well today: ....

....

Blah: ....

....

MOODS

HABITS

SUNDAY in a sentence: ....

....

What's good about my life: ....

....

What I did well today: ....

....

Blah: ....

....

MOODS

HABITS

Week In Review: ....

YA WIN SOME, YA LOSE SOME
The best & worst of this week

YAY!

BOO!

RATE THIS WEEK'S
OVERALL HAPPYISHNESS:

UN-HAPPYISH   HAPPYISH

Week Of:

MONDAY in a sentence:...

....

What's good about my life:...

What I did well today:...

....

Blah:...

....

MOODS

HABITS

TUESDAY in a sentence:...

What's good about my life:...

....

What I did well today:...

Blah:...

....

MOODS

HABITS

WEDNESDAY in a sentence:.......................................

....

What's good about my life:...

....

What I did well today:...

Blah:...

....

MOODS

HABITS

THURSDAY in a sentence:...

....

What's good about my life:...

What I did well today:...

....

Blah:...

....

MOODS

HABITS

FRIDAY in a sentence: ....

....

What's good about my life: ....

....

MOODS

What I did well today: ....

....

Blah: ....

....

HABITS

SATURDAY in a sentence: ....

....

What's good about my life: ....

....

MOODS

What I did well today: ....

....

Blah: ....

....

HABITS

SUNDAY in a sentence: ....

....

What's good about my life: ....

....

MOODS

What I did well today: ....

....

Blah: ....

....

HABITS

Week In Review: ....

YA WIN SOME, YA LOSE SOME
The best & worst of this week

RATE THIS WEEK'S
OVERALL HAPPYISHNESS:

YAY!   BOO!

UN-HAPPYISH   HAPPYISH

Week Of:

MONDAY in a sentence: ....

....

What's good about my life: ....

What I did well today: ....

....

Blah: ....

MOODS

HABITS

TUESDAY in a sentence: ....

What's good about my life: ....

....

What I did well today: ....

Blah: ....

MOODS

HABITS

WEDNESDAY in a sentence: ....

....

What's good about my life: ....

....

What I did well today: ....

....

Blah: ....

....

MOODS

HABITS

THURSDAY in a sentence: ....

....

What's good about my life: ....

What I did well today: ....

....

Blah: ....

....

MOODS

HABITS

FRIDAY in a sentence: ....

....

What's good about my life: ....

....

What I did well today: ....

....

Blah: ....

....

MOODS ○ ○ ○ ○

HABITS ○ ○ ○ ○

SATURDAY in a sentence: ....

....

What's good about my life: ....

....

What I did well today: ....

....

Blah: ....

....

MOODS ○ ○ ○ ○

HABITS ○ ○ ○ ○

SUNDAY in a sentence: ....

....

What's good about my life: ....

....

What I did well today: ....

....

Blah: ....

....

MOODS ○ ○ ○ ○

HABITS ○ ○ ○ ○

Week In Review: ....

YA WIN SOME, YA LOSE SOME
The best & worst of this week

YAY!

BOO!

RATE THIS WEEK'S
OVERALL HAPPYISHNESS:

UN-HAPPYISH   HAPPYISH

Week Of:

MONDAY in a sentence: ....

....

What's good about my life: ....

....

What I did well today: ....

....

Blah: ....

....

MOODS

HABITS

TUESDAY in a sentence: ....

....

What's good about my life: ....

....

What I did well today: ....

....

Blah: ....

....

MOODS

HABITS

WEDNESDAY in a sentence: ....

....

What's good about my life: ....

....

What I did well today: ....

....

Blah: ....

....

MOODS

HABITS

THURSDAY in a sentence: ....

....

What's good about my life: ....

....

What I did well today: ....

....

Blah: ....

....

MOODS

HABITS

FRIDAY in a sentence: ....

....

What's good about my life: ....

....

What I did well today: ....

....

Blah: ....

....

MOODS

○ ○ ○ ○

HABITS

○ ○ ○ ○

SATURDAY in a sentence: ....

....

What's good about my life: ....

....

What I did well today: ....

....

Blah: ....

....

MOODS

○ ○ ○ ○

HABITS

○ ○ ○ ○

SUNDAY in a sentence: ....

....

What's good about my life: ....

....

What I did well today: ....

....

Blah: ....

....

MOODS

○ ○ ○ ○

HABITS

○ ○ ○ ○

Week In Review: ....

YA WIN SOME, YA LOSE SOME
The best & worst of this week

YAY!

BOO!

RATE THIS WEEK'S
OVERALL HAPPYISHNESS:

UN-HAPPYISH   HAPPYISH

Month In Review:

QUIT LIST: What are the things/people/actions/thoughts you can quit this month: the weekly yoga class you dread? The coffee shop with the rude baristas? Your morning doomscroll? These are tangible changes you can make... but you don't have to!

I quit... ....

....

....

....

....

BRAGGABLE: Please save your humble pie for another occasion. This is a space to tell yourself everything you did well this month. Like, everything. You flossed once? You didn't roll your eyes at your annoying neighbor? You told your partner exactly why you were angry instead of making them guess? WELL DONE!

I feel great about... ....

....

....

....

....

LET IT BURN: Let's not pretend that everything is perfect or fine or just dandy. Here's a space for you to write down all your icky stuff: the jealous feelings that make you feel gross, the negative things you say to yourself, the texts you wanted to send but didn't, because you knew it was totally inappropriate. Write it down. Tear it out. Burn it up. Or just fold the page over. The point is... these are the things you can let go.

I acknowledge & let go of... ....

....

....

....

THERE IS NO YARDSTICK FOR SUFFERING,

and if there were, I wouldn't want to use it anyway. The worst thing that has happened to you is the worst thing that has happened to you. My suffering can't make yours any easier or harder. The weight is relative. It is non-transferable, it is not converted from ounces to grams or inches to centimeters, Celsius to Fahrenheit. If it's heavy for you, it's heavy. If it's big for you, it's big. If it burns you, it's hot.

Week Of:

MONDAY in a sentence: ....

....

What's good about my life: ....

....

What I did well today: ....

....

Blah: ....

....

MOODS

HABITS

TUESDAY in a sentence: ....

....

What's good about my life: ....

....

What I did well today: ....

....

Blah: ....

....

MOODS

HABITS

WEDNESDAY in a sentence: ....

....

What's good about my life: ....

....

What I did well today: ....

....

Blah: ....

....

MOODS

HABITS

THURSDAY in a sentence: ....

....

What's good about my life: ....

....

What I did well today: ....

....

Blah: ....

....

MOODS

HABITS

FRIDAY in a sentence: ....

What's good about my life: ....

What I did well today: ....

Blah: ....

MOODS ○ ○ ○ ○

HABITS ○ ○ ○ ○

SATURDAY in a sentence: ....

What's good about my life: ....

What I did well today: ....

Blah: ....

MOODS ○ ○ ○ ○

HABITS ○ ○ ○ ○

SUNDAY in a sentence: ....

What's good about my life: ....

What I did well today: ....

Blah: ....

MOODS ○ ○ ○ ○

HABITS ○ ○ ○ ○

Week In Review: ....

YA WIN SOME, YA LOSE SOME
The best & worst of this week

YAY!

BOO!

RATE THIS WEEK'S OVERALL HAPPYISHNESS:

UN-HAPPYISH   HAPPYISH

Week Of:

MONDAY in a sentence:..

....

What's good about my life:...

....

What I did well today:..

....

Blah:..

MOODS

HABITS

TUESDAY in a sentence:..

....

What's good about my life:...

....

What I did well today:..

....

Blah:..

MOODS

HABITS

WEDNESDAY in a sentence:..

....

What's good about my life:...

....

What I did well today:..

....

Blah:..

MOODS

HABITS

THURSDAY in a sentence:...

....

What's good about my life:...

....

What I did well today:..

....

Blah:..

MOODS

HABITS

FRIDAY in a sentence: ....

....

What's good about my life: ....

....

What I did well today: ....

....

Blah: ....

....

MOODS

HABITS

SATURDAY in a sentence: ....

....

What's good about my life: ....

....

What I did well today: ....

....

Blah: ....

....

MOODS

HABITS

SUNDAY in a sentence: ....

....

What's good about my life: ....

....

What I did well today: ....

....

Blah: ....

....

MOODS

HABITS

Week In Review: ....

YA WIN SOME, YA LOSE SOME
The best & worst of this week

YAY!   BOO!

RATE THIS WEEK'S
OVERALL HAPPYISHNESS:

UN-HAPPYISH   HAPPYISH

Week Of:

MONDAY in a sentence: ....

....

What's good about my life: ....

....

What I did well today: ....

....

Blah: ....

....

MOODS

HABITS

TUESDAY in a sentence: ....

....

What's good about my life: ....

....

What I did well today: ....

....

Blah: ....

....

MOODS

HABITS

WEDNESDAY in a sentence: ....

....

What's good about my life: ....

....

What I did well today: ....

....

Blah: ....

....

MOODS

HABITS

THURSDAY in a sentence: ....

....

What's good about my life: ....

....

What I did well today: ....

....

Blah: ....

....

MOODS

HABITS

FRIDAY in a sentence: ....

....

What's good about my life: ....

....

What I did well today: ....

....

Blah: ....

....

SATURDAY in a sentence: ....

....

What's good about my life: ....

....

What I did well today: ....

....

Blah: ....

....

SUNDAY in a sentence: ....

....

What's good about my life: ....

....

What I did well today: ....

....

Blah: ....

....

Week In Review: ....

YA WIN SOME, YA LOSE SOME
The best & worst of this week

YAY!   BOO!

**RATE THIS WEEK'S
OVERALL HAPPYISHNESS:**

UN-HAPPYISH   HAPPYISH

Week Of:

MONDAY in a sentence: ....

....

What's good about my life: ....

....

What I did well today: ....

....

Blah: ....

....

MOODS

HABITS

TUESDAY in a sentence: ....

....

What's good about my life: ....

....

What I did well today: ....

....

Blah: ....

....

MOODS

HABITS

WEDNESDAY in a sentence: ....

....

What's good about my life: ....

....

What I did well today: ....

....

Blah: ....

....

MOODS

HABITS

THURSDAY in a sentence: ....

....

What's good about my life: ....

....

What I did well today: ....

....

Blah: ....

....

MOODS

HABITS

FRIDAY in a sentence: ....

....

What's good about my life: ....

....

What I did well today: ....

....

Blah: ....

....

MOODS ○ ○ ○ ○

HABITS ○ ○ ○ ○

SATURDAY in a sentence: ....

....

What's good about my life: ....

....

What I did well today: ....

....

Blah: ....

....

MOODS ○ ○ ○ ○

HABITS ○ ○ ○ ○

SUNDAY in a sentence: ....

....

What's good about my life: ....

....

What I did well today: ....

....

Blah: ....

....

MOODS ○ ○ ○ ○

HABITS ○ ○ ○ ○

Week In Review: ....

YA WIN SOME, YA LOSE SOME
The best & worst of this week

YAY!

BOO!

RATE THIS WEEK'S
OVERALL HAPPYISHNESS:

UN-HAPPYISH   HAPPYISH

QUIT LIST: What are the things/people/actions/thoughts you can quit this month: the weekly yoga class you dread? The coffee shop with the rude baristas? Your morning doomscroll? These are tangible changes you can make... but you don't have to!

I quit... ....

....

....

....

....

BRAGGABLE: Please save your humble pie for another occasion. This is a space to tell yourself everything you did well this month. Like, everything. You flossed once? You didn't roll your eyes at your annoying neighbor? You told your partner exactly why you were angry instead of making them guess? WELL DONE!

I feel great about... ....

....

....

....

....

LET IT BURN: Let's not pretend that everything is perfect or fine or just dandy. Here's a space for you to write down all your icky stuff: the jealous feelings that make you feel gross, the negative things you say to yourself, the texts you wanted to send but didn't, because you knew it was totally inappropriate. Write it down. Tear it out. Burn it up. Or just fold the page over. The point is... these are the things you can let go.

I acknowledge & let go of... ....

....

....

....

....

WE ARE ALLOWED

to hold our own experience up to the light and decide what to call it, to define it for ourselves and explain that meaning to the people around us.

Week Of:

MONDAY in a sentence: ....

....

What's good about my life: ....

What I did well today: ....

....

Blah: ....

....

MOODS

HABITS

TUESDAY in a sentence: ....

....

What's good about my life: ....

....

What I did well today: ....

....

Blah: ....

....

MOODS

HABITS

WEDNESDAY in a sentence: ....

....

What's good about my life: ....

....

What I did well today: ....

....

Blah: ....

....

MOODS

HABITS

THURSDAY in a sentence: ....

....

What's good about my life: ....

What I did well today: ....

....

Blah: ....

....

MOODS

HABITS

FRIDAY in a sentence: ....

....

What's good about my life: ....

....

What I did well today: ....

....

Blah: ....

....

MOODS

HABITS

SATURDAY in a sentence: ....

....

What's good about my life: ....

....

What I did well today: ....

....

Blah: ....

....

MOODS

HABITS

SUNDAY in a sentence: ....

....

What's good about my life: ....

....

What I did well today: ....

....

Blah: ....

....

MOODS

HABITS

Week In Review: ....

YA WIN SOME, YA LOSE SOME
The best & worst of this week

YAY!

BOO!

RATE THIS WEEK'S
OVERALL HAPPYISHNESS:

UN-HAPPYISH   HAPPYISH

Week Of: ....

MONDAY in a sentence: ....

....

What's good about my life: ....

....

What I did well today: ....

....

Blah: ....

....

MOODS ○ ○ ○ ○

HABITS ○ ○ ○ ○

TUESDAY in a sentence: ....

....

What's good about my life: ....

....

What I did well today: ....

....

Blah: ....

....

MOODS ○ ○ ○ ○

HABITS ○ ○ ○ ○

WEDNESDAY in a sentence: ....

....

What's good about my life: ....

....

What I did well today: ....

....

Blah: ....

....

MOODS ○ ○ ○ ○

HABITS ○ ○ ○ ○

THURSDAY in a sentence: ....

....

What's good about my life: ....

....

What I did well today: ....

....

Blah: ....

....

MOODS ○ ○ ○ ○

HABITS ○ ○ ○ ○

FRIDAY in a sentence: ....

....

What's good about my life: ....

....

What I did well today: ....

....

Blah: ....

....

MOODS ○ ○ ○ ○

HABITS ○ ○ ○ ○

SATURDAY in a sentence: ....

....

What's good about my life: ....

....

What I did well today: ....

....

Blah: ....

....

MOODS ○ ○ ○ ○

HABITS ○ ○ ○ ○

SUNDAY in a sentence: ....

....

What's good about my life: ....

....

What I did well today: ....

....

Blah: ....

....

MOODS ○ ○ ○ ○

HABITS ○ ○ ○ ○

Week In Review: ....

YA WIN SOME, YA LOSE SOME
The best & worst of this week

YAY!

BOO!

RATE THIS WEEK'S
OVERALL HAPPYISHNESS:

UN-HAPPYISH   HAPPYISH

Week Of:

MONDAY in a sentence:

What's good about my life:

What I did well today:

Blah:

MOODS

HABITS

TUESDAY in a sentence:

What's good about my life:

What I did well today:

Blah:

MOODS

HABITS

WEDNESDAY in a sentence:

What's good about my life:

What I did well today:

Blah:

MOODS

HABITS

THURSDAY in a sentence:

What's good about my life:

What I did well today:

Blah:

MOODS

HABITS

FRIDAY in a sentence: ....

What's good about my life: ....

What I did well today: ....

Blah: ....

MOODS ○ ○ ○ ○

HABITS ○ ○ ○ ○

SATURDAY in a sentence: ....

What's good about my life: ....

What I did well today: ....

Blah: ....

MOODS ○ ○ ○ ○

HABITS ○ ○ ○ ○

SUNDAY in a sentence: ....

What's good about my life: ....

What I did well today: ....

Blah: ....

MOODS ○ ○ ○ ○

HABITS ○ ○ ○ ○

Week In Review: ....

YA WIN SOME, YA LOSE SOME
The best & worst of this week

YAY!

BOO!

**RATE THIS WEEK'S
OVERALL HAPPYISHNESS:**

UN-HAPPYISH   HAPPYISH

Week Of:

MONDAY in a sentence: ....

....

What's good about my life: ....

What I did well today: ....

....

Blah: ....

MOODS

HABITS

TUESDAY in a sentence: ....

....

What's good about my life: ....

....

What I did well today: ....

....

Blah: ....

....

MOODS

HABITS

WEDNESDAY in a sentence: ....

....

What's good about my life: ....

....

What I did well today: ....

Blah: ....

MOODS

HABITS

THURSDAY in a sentence: ....

....

What's good about my life: ....

MOODS

What I did well today: ....

Blah: ....

HABITS

FRIDAY in a sentence: ....

....

What's good about my life: ....

....

What I did well today: ....

....

Blah: ....

....

MOODS

HABITS

SATURDAY in a sentence: ....

....

What's good about my life: ....

....

What I did well today: ....

....

Blah: ....

....

MOODS

HABITS

SUNDAY in a sentence: ....

....

What's good about my life: ....

....

What I did well today: ....

....

Blah: ....

....

MOODS

HABITS

Week In Review: ....

YA WIN SOME, YA LOSE SOME
The best & worst of this week

YAY!

BOO!

RATE THIS WEEK'S
OVERALL HAPPYISHNESS:

UN-HAPPYISH   HAPPYISH

QUIT LIST: What are the things/people/actions/thoughts you can quit this month: the weekly yoga class you dread? The coffee shop with the rude baristas? Your morning doomscroll? These are tangible changes you can make... but you don't have to!

I quit... ....

....

....

....

....

BRAGGABLE: Please save your humble pie for another occasion. This is a space to tell yourself everything you did well this month. Like, everything. You flossed once? You didn't roll your eyes at your annoying neighbor? You told your partner exactly why you were angry instead of making them guess? WELL DONE!

I feel great about... ....

....

....

....

....

LET IT BURN: Let's not pretend that everything is perfect or fine or just dandy. Here's a space for you to write down all your icky stuff: the jealous feelings that make you feel gross, the negative things you say to yourself, the texts you wanted to send but didn't, because you knew it was totally inappropriate. Write it down. Tear it out. Burn it up. Or just fold the page over. The point is... these are the things you can let go.

I acknowledge & let go of... ....

....

....

....

....

YOUR SUFFERING IS NOT A SELF-IMPROVEMENT EXERCISE.

Week Of:

MONDAY in a sentence: ....
....

What's good about my life: ....

What I did well today: ....
....

Blah: ....
....

MOODS

HABITS

TUESDAY in a sentence: ....
....

What's good about my life: ....

What I did well today: ....
....

Blah: ....
....

MOODS

HABITS

WEDNESDAY in a sentence: ....
....

What's good about my life: ....

What I did well today: ....
....

Blah: ....
....

MOODS

HABITS

THURSDAY in a sentence: ....
....

What's good about my life: ....

What I did well today: ....
....

Blah: ....
....

MOODS

HABITS

FRIDAY in a sentence: ....

....

What's good about my life: ....

....

What I did well today: ....

....

Blah: ....

....

MOODS ○ ○ ○ ○

HABITS ○ ○ ○ ○

SATURDAY in a sentence: ....

....

What's good about my life: ....

....

What I did well today: ....

....

Blah: ....

....

MOODS ○ ○ ○ ○

HABITS ○ ○ ○ ○

SUNDAY in a sentence: ....

....

What's good about my life: ....

....

What I did well today: ....

....

Blah: ....

....

MOODS ○ ○ ○ ○

HABITS ○ ○ ○ ○

Week In Review: ....

YA WIN SOME, YA LOSE SOME
The best & worst of this week

YAY!

BOO!

RATE THIS WEEK'S OVERALL HAPPYISHNESS:

UN-HAPPYISH   HAPPYISH

Week Of: ....

MONDAY in a sentence: ....
....

What's good about my life: ....

What I did well today: ....

Blah: ....

MOODS

HABITS

TUESDAY in a sentence: ....
....

What's good about my life: ....

What I did well today: ....

Blah: ....

MOODS

HABITS

WEDNESDAY in a sentence: ....
....

What's good about my life: ....

What I did well today: ....

Blah: ....

MOODS

HABITS

THURSDAY in a sentence: ....
....

What's good about my life: ....

What I did well today: ....

Blah: ....

MOODS

HABITS

FRIDAY in a sentence: ....

....

What's good about my life: ....

....

What I did well today: ....

....

Blah: ....

....

MOODS

HABITS

SATURDAY in a sentence: ....

....

What's good about my life: ....

....

What I did well today: ....

....

Blah: ....

....

MOODS

HABITS

SUNDAY in a sentence: ....

....

What's good about my life: ....

....

What I did well today: ....

....

Blah: ....

....

MOODS

HABITS

Week In Review: ....

YA WIN SOME, YA LOSE SOME
The best & worst of this week

YAY!

BOO!

RATE THIS WEEK'S
OVERALL HAPPYISHNESS:

UN-HAPPYISH   HAPPYISH

Week Of:

MONDAY in a sentence:

What's good about my life:

MOODS ○ ○ ○ ○

What I did well today:

HABITS ○ ○ ○ ○

Blah:

TUESDAY in a sentence:

What's good about my life:

MOODS ○ ○ ○ ○

What I did well today:

HABITS ○ ○ ○ ○

Blah:

WEDNESDAY in a sentence:

What's good about my life:

MOODS ○ ○ ○ ○

What I did well today:

HABITS ○ ○ ○ ○

Blah:

THURSDAY in a sentence:

What's good about my life:

MOODS ○ ○ ○ ○

What I did well today:

HABITS ○ ○ ○ ○

Blah:

FRIDAY in a sentence: ....

....

What's good about my life: ....

....

What I did well today: ....

....

Blah: ....

....

MOODS ○ ○ ○ ○

HABITS ○ ○ ○ ○

SATURDAY in a sentence: ....

....

What's good about my life: ....

....

What I did well today: ....

....

Blah: ....

....

MOODS ○ ○ ○ ○

HABITS ○ ○ ○ ○

SUNDAY in a sentence: ....

....

What's good about my life: ....

....

What I did well today: ....

....

Blah: ....

....

MOODS ○ ○ ○ ○

HABITS ○ ○ ○ ○

Week In Review: ....

YA WIN SOME, YA LOSE SOME
The best & worst of this week

RATE THIS WEEK'S
OVERALL HAPPYISHNESS:

YAY!

BOO!

UN-HAPPYISH   HAPPYISH

Week Of: ....

MONDAY in a sentence: ....

....

What's good about my life: ....

....

What I did well today: ....

....

Blah: ....

○ ○ ○ ○ **MOODS**

○ ○ ○ ○ **HABITS**

TUESDAY in a sentence: ....

....

What's good about my life: ....

....

What I did well today: ....

....

Blah: ....

○ ○ ○ ○ **MOODS**

○ ○ ○ ○ **HABITS**

WEDNESDAY in a sentence: ....

....

What's good about my life: ....

....

What I did well today: ....

....

Blah: ....

○ ○ ○ ○ **MOODS**

○ ○ ○ ○ **HABITS**

THURSDAY in a sentence: ....

....

What's good about my life: ....

....

What I did well today: ....

....

Blah: ....

○ ○ ○ ○ **MOODS**

○ ○ ○ ○ **HABITS**

FRIDAY in a sentence: ....

....

What's good about my life: ....

....

What I did well today: ....

....

Blah: ....

....

MOODS ○ ○ ○ ○

HABITS ○ ○ ○ ○

SATURDAY in a sentence: ....

....

What's good about my life: ....

....

What I did well today: ....

....

Blah: ....

....

MOODS ○ ○ ○ ○

HABITS ○ ○ ○ ○

SUNDAY in a sentence: ....

....

What's good about my life: ....

....

What I did well today: ....

....

Blah: ....

....

MOODS ○ ○ ○ ○

HABITS ○ ○ ○ ○

Week In Review: ....

YA WIN SOME, YA LOSE SOME
The best & worst of this week

YAY!

BOO!

RATE THIS WEEK'S OVERALL HAPPYISHNESS:

UN-HAPPYISH   HAPPYISH

Month In Review:

QUIT LIST: What are the things/people/actions/thoughts you can quit this month: the weekly yoga class you dread? The coffee shop with the rude baristas? Your morning doomscroll? These are tangible changes you can make... but you don't have to!

I quit... ....

....

....

....

BRAGGABLE: Please save your humble pie for another occasion. This is a space to tell yourself everything you did well this month. Like, everything. You flossed once? You didn't roll your eyes at your annoying neighbor? You told your partner exactly why you were angry instead of making them guess? WELL DONE!

I feel great about... ....

....

....

....

LET IT BURN: Let's not pretend that everything is perfect or fine or just dandy. Here's a space for you to write down all your icky stuff: the jealous feelings that make you feel gross, the negative things you say to yourself, the texts you wanted to send but didn't, because you knew it was totally inappropriate. Write it down. Tear it out. Burn it up. Or just fold the page over. The point is... these are the things you can let go.

I acknowledge & let go of... ....

....

....

....

TO PRETEND THAT ANYONE IS JUST ONE THING

is to deny the fullness of our humanity—that we are sometimes the victim and sometimes the villain, that we can do the unforgivable and still be worthy of love, of compassion, of forgiveness.

Week Of: ....

MONDAY in a sentence: ....
....

MOODS

What's good about my life: ....
....

What I did well today: ....
....

HABITS

Blah: ....
....

TUESDAY in a sentence: ....
....

MOODS

What's good about my life: ....
....

What I did well today: ....
....

HABITS

Blah: ....
....

WEDNESDAY in a sentence: ....
....

MOODS

What's good about my life: ....
....

What I did well today: ....
....

HABITS

Blah: ....

THURSDAY in a sentence: ....
....

MOODS

What's good about my life: ....
....

What I did well today: ....
....

HABITS

Blah: ....

FRIDAY in a sentence: ....
....

What's good about my life: ....

What I did well today: ....

Blah: ....
....

MOODS

HABITS

SATURDAY in a sentence: ....
....

What's good about my life: ....

What I did well today: ....

Blah: ....
....

MOODS

HABITS

SUNDAY in a sentence: ....
....

What's good about my life: ....

What I did well today: ....

Blah: ....
....

MOODS

HABITS

Week In Review: ....

YA WIN SOME, YA LOSE SOME
The best & worst of this week

YAY!

BOO!

RATE THIS WEEK'S
OVERALL HAPPYISHNESS:

UN-HAPPYISH   HAPPYISH

Week Of:

MONDAY in a sentence:

....

What's good about my life:

....

What I did well today:

....

Blah:

....

MOODS

HABITS

TUESDAY in a sentence:

....

What's good about my life:

....

What I did well today:

....

Blah:

....

MOODS

HABITS

WEDNESDAY in a sentence:

....

What's good about my life:

....

What I did well today:

....

Blah:

....

MOODS

HABITS

THURSDAY in a sentence:

....

What's good about my life:

....

What I did well today:

....

Blah:

....

MOODS

HABITS

FRIDAY in a sentence: ....

What's good about my life: ....

What I did well today: ....

Blah: ....

MOODS

HABITS

SATURDAY in a sentence: ....

What's good about my life: ....

What I did well today: ....

Blah: ....

MOODS

HABITS

SUNDAY in a sentence: ....

What's good about my life: ....

What I did well today: ....

Blah: ....

MOODS

HABITS

Week In Review:

YA WIN SOME, YA LOSE SOME
The best & worst of this week

YAY!

BOO!

RATE THIS WEEK'S
OVERALL HAPPYISHNESS:

UN-HAPPYISH   HAPPYISH

Week Of: ....

MONDAY in a sentence: ....
....

What's good about my life: ....

What I did well today: ....

Blah: ....
....

MOODS ○ ○ ○ ○

HABITS ○ ○ ○ ○

TUESDAY in a sentence: ....
....

What's good about my life: ....

What I did well today: ....

Blah: ....
....

MOODS ○ ○ ○ ○

HABITS ○ ○ ○ ○

WEDNESDAY in a sentence: ....
....

What's good about my life: ....

What I did well today: ....

Blah: ....
....

MOODS ○ ○ ○ ○

HABITS ○ ○ ○ ○

THURSDAY in a sentence: ....
....

What's good about my life: ....

What I did well today: ....

Blah: ....
....

MOODS ○ ○ ○ ○

HABITS ○ ○ ○ ○

FRIDAY in a sentence: ....

....

What's good about my life: ....

What I did well today: ....

Blah: ....

....

MOODS

HABITS

SATURDAY in a sentence: ....

What's good about my life: ....

....

What I did well today: ....

Blah: ....

....

MOODS

HABITS

SUNDAY in a sentence: ....

What's good about my life: ....

....

What I did well today: ....

Blah: ....

....

MOODS

HABITS

Week In Review: ....

YA WIN SOME, YA LOSE SOME
The best & worst of this week

YAY!

BOO!

RATE THIS WEEK'S
OVERALL HAPPYISHNESS:

UN-HAPPYISH   HAPPYISH

Week Of:

MONDAY in a sentence:..

....

What's good about my life:...

....

What I did well today:..

....

Blah:...

MOODS

HABITS

TUESDAY in a sentence:...

....

What's good about my life:...

....

What I did well today:..

....

Blah:...

....

MOODS

HABITS

WEDNESDAY in a sentence:..

....

What's good about my life:...

....

What I did well today:..

....

Blah:...

....

MOODS

HABITS

THURSDAY in a sentence:...

....

What's good about my life:...

What I did well today:..

....

Blah:...

....

MOODS

HABITS

FRIDAY in a sentence: ....

What's good about my life: ....

What I did well today: ....

Blah: ....

MOODS

HABITS

SATURDAY in a sentence: ....

What's good about my life: ....

What I did well today: ....

Blah: ....

MOODS

HABITS

SUNDAY in a sentence: ....

What's good about my life: ....

What I did well today: ....

Blah: ....

MOODS

HABITS

Week In Review: ....

YA WIN SOME, YA LOSE SOME
The best & worst of this week

YAY!

BOO!

**RATE THIS WEEK'S
OVERALL HAPPYISHNESS:**

UN-HAPPYISH   HAPPYISH

QUIT LIST: What are the things/people/actions/thoughts you can quit this month: the weekly yoga class you dread? The coffee shop with the rude baristas? Your morning doomscroll? These are tangible changes you can make... but you don't have to!

I quit... ....

....

....

....

....

BRAGGABLE: Please save your humble pie for another occasion. This is a space to tell yourself everything you did well this month. Like, everything. You flossed once? You didn't roll your eyes at your annoying neighbor? You told your partner exactly why you were angry instead of making them guess? WELL DONE!

I feel great about... ....

....

....

....

....

LET IT BURN: Let's not pretend that everything is perfect or fine or just dandy. Here's a space for you to write down all your icky stuff: the jealous feelings that make you feel gross, the negative things you say to yourself, the texts you wanted to send but didn't, because you knew it was totally inappropriate. Write it down. Tear it out. Burn it up. Or just fold the page over. The point is... these are the things you can let go.

I acknowledge & let go of... ....

....

....

....

DON'T "SHOULD" YOURSELF. SERIOUSLY, IF YOU WERE EVEN THINKING ABOUT IT, DON'T.

Week Of:

MONDAY in a sentence: ....

....

What's good about my life: ....

What I did well today: ....

Blah: ....

MOODS ○ ○ ○ ○

HABITS ○ ○ ○ ○

TUESDAY in a sentence: ....

....

What's good about my life: ....

What I did well today: ....

Blah: ....

MOODS ○ ○ ○ ○

HABITS ○ ○ ○ ○

WEDNESDAY in a sentence: ....

....

What's good about my life: ....

What I did well today: ....

Blah: ....

MOODS ○ ○ ○ ○

HABITS ○ ○ ○ ○

THURSDAY in a sentence: ....

....

What's good about my life: ....

What I did well today: ....

Blah: ....

MOODS ○ ○ ○ ○

HABITS ○ ○ ○ ○

FRIDAY in a sentence: ....

....

What's good about my life: ....

What I did well today: ....

Blah: ....

MOODS ○ ○ ○ ○

HABITS ○ ○ ○ ○

SATURDAY in a sentence: ....

What's good about my life: ....

What I did well today: ....

Blah: ....

MOODS ○ ○ ○ ○

HABITS ○ ○ ○ ○

SUNDAY in a sentence: ....

What's good about my life: ....

What I did well today: ....

Blah: ....

MOODS ○ ○ ○ ○

HABITS ○ ○ ○ ○

Week In Review: ....

YA WIN SOME, YA LOSE SOME
The best & worst of this week

YAY!

BOO!

RATE THIS WEEK'S OVERALL HAPPYISHNESS:

UN-HAPPYISH   HAPPYISH

Week Of:

MONDAY in a sentence:

What's good about my life:

What I did well today:

Blah:

MOODS

HABITS

TUESDAY in a sentence:

What's good about my life:

What I did well today:

Blah:

MOODS

HABITS

WEDNESDAY in a sentence:

What's good about my life:

What I did well today:

Blah:

MOODS

HABITS

THURSDAY in a sentence:

What's good about my life:

What I did well today:

Blah:

MOODS

HABITS

FRIDAY in a sentence: ....

.... MOODS

What's good about my life: ....

....

What I did well today: .... HABITS

....

Blah: ....

....

SATURDAY in a sentence: ....

.... MOODS

What's good about my life: ....

....

What I did well today: .... HABITS

....

Blah: ....

....

SUNDAY in a sentence: ....

.... MOODS

What's good about my life: ....

....

What I did well today: .... HABITS

....

Blah: ....

....

Week In Review: ....

YA WIN SOME, YA LOSE SOME
The best & worst of this week

YAY!   **BOO!**

RATE THIS WEEK'S
OVERALL HAPPYISHNESS:

UN-HAPPYISH   HAPPYISH

Week Of: ....

MONDAY in a sentence: ....
....

What's good about my life: ....

What I did well today: ....

Blah: ....

MOODS

○ ○ ○ ○

HABITS

○ ○ ○ ○

TUESDAY in a sentence: ....
....

What's good about my life: ....

What I did well today: ....

Blah: ....

MOODS

○ ○ ○ ○

HABITS

○ ○ ○ ○

WEDNESDAY in a sentence: ....
....

What's good about my life: ....

What I did well today: ....

Blah: ....

MOODS

○ ○ ○ ○

HABITS

○ ○ ○ ○

THURSDAY in a sentence: ....

What's good about my life: ....

What I did well today: ....

Blah: ....
....

MOODS

○ ○ ○ ○

HABITS

○ ○ ○ ○

FRIDAY in a sentence: ....

What's good about my life: ....

What I did well today: ....

Blah: ....
....

MOODS

HABITS

SATURDAY in a sentence: ....

....

What's good about my life: ....

What I did well today: ....

Blah: ....
....

MOODS

HABITS

SUNDAY in a sentence: ....

....

What's good about my life: ....

What I did well today: ....

Blah: ....
....

MOODS

HABITS

Week In Review: ....

YA WIN SOME, YA LOSE SOME
The best & worst of this week

YAY!

BOO!

RATE THIS WEEK'S
OVERALL HAPPYISHNESS:

UN-HAPPYISH   HAPPYISH

Week Of:

MONDAY in a sentence:

What's good about my life:

What I did well today:

Blah:

MOODS

HABITS

TUESDAY in a sentence:

What's good about my life:

What I did well today:

Blah:

MOODS

HABITS

WEDNESDAY in a sentence:

What's good about my life:

What I did well today:

Blah:

MOODS

HABITS

THURSDAY in a sentence:

What's good about my life:

What I did well today:

Blah:

MOODS

HABITS

FRIDAY in a sentence: ....

....

What's good about my life: ....

....

What I did well today: ....

....

Blah: ....

....

MOODS

HABITS

SATURDAY in a sentence: ....

....

What's good about my life: ....

....

What I did well today: ....

....

Blah: ....

....

MOODS

HABITS

SUNDAY in a sentence: ....

....

What's good about my life: ....

....

What I did well today: ....

....

Blah: ....

....

MOODS

HABITS

Week In Review: ....

YA WIN SOME, YA LOSE SOME
The best & worst of this week

YAY!

BOO!

RATE THIS WEEK'S
OVERALL HAPPYISHNESS:

UN-HAPPYISH   HAPPYISH

QUIT LIST: What are the things/people/actions/thoughts you can quit this month: the weekly yoga class you dread? The coffee shop with the rude baristas? Your morning doomscroll? These are tangible changes you can make... but you don't have to!

I quit... ....

....

....

....

....

BRAGGABLE: Please save your humble pie for another occasion. This is a space to tell yourself everything you did well this month. Like, everything. You flossed once? You didn't roll your eyes at your annoying neighbor? You told your partner exactly why you were angry instead of making them guess? WELL DONE!

I feel great about... ....

....

....

....

....

LET IT BURN: Let's not pretend that everything is perfect or fine or just dandy. Here's a space for you to write down all your icky stuff: the jealous feelings that make you feel gross, the negative things you say to yourself, the texts you wanted to send but didn't, because you knew it was totally inappropriate. Write it down. Tear it out. Burn it up. Or just fold the page over. The point is... these are the things you can let go.

I acknowledge & let go of... ....

....

....

....

....

YOU KNEW WHAT YOU KNEW.

You did what you did. You were not able to fast-forward. You lived at the exact speed of life and not a moment faster.

Week Of:

MONDAY in a sentence:

What's good about my life:

What I did well today:

Blah:

MOODS

HABITS

TUESDAY in a sentence:

What's good about my life:

What I did well today:

Blah:

MOODS

HABITS

WEDNESDAY in a sentence:

What's good about my life:

What I did well today:

Blah:

MOODS

HABITS

THURSDAY in a sentence:

What's good about my life:

What I did well today:

Blah:

MOODS

HABITS

FRIDAY in a sentence: ....

....

What's good about my life: ....

What I did well today: ....

Blah: ....

....

MOODS

HABITS

SATURDAY in a sentence: ....

....

What's good about my life: ....

What I did well today: ....

Blah: ....

....

MOODS

HABITS

SUNDAY in a sentence: ....

....

What's good about my life: ....

What I did well today: ....

Blah: ....

....

MOODS

HABITS

Week In Review: ....

YA WIN SOME, YA LOSE SOME
The best & worst of this week

RATE THIS WEEK'S
OVERALL HAPPYISHNESS:

YAY!

BOO!

UN-HAPPYISH   HAPPYISH

Week Of:

MONDAY in a sentence: ....

....

What's good about my life: ....

....

What I did well today: ....

....

Blah: ....

....

MOODS

HABITS

TUESDAY in a sentence: ....

....

What's good about my life: ....

....

What I did well today: ....

....

Blah: ....

....

MOODS

HABITS

WEDNESDAY in a sentence: ....

....

What's good about my life: ....

....

What I did well today: ....

....

Blah: ....

....

MOODS

HABITS

THURSDAY in a sentence: ....

....

What's good about my life: ....

....

What I did well today: ....

....

Blah: ....

....

MOODS

HABITS

FRIDAY in a sentence: ....

....

What's good about my life: ....

....

What I did well today: ....

....

Blah: ....

....

MOODS

HABITS

SATURDAY in a sentence: ....

....

What's good about my life: ....

....

What I did well today: ....

....

Blah: ....

....

MOODS

HABITS

SUNDAY in a sentence: ....

....

What's good about my life: ....

....

What I did well today: ....

....

Blah: ....

....

MOODS

HABITS

Week In Review: ....

YA WIN SOME, YA LOSE SOME
The best & worst of this week

YAY**!**

BOO**!**

RATE THIS WEEK'S
OVERALL HAPPYISHNESS:

UN-HAPPYISH   HAPPYISH

Week Of: ....

MONDAY in a sentence: ....

....

What's good about my life: ....

....

What I did well today: ....

....

Blah: ....

....

MOODS

HABITS

TUESDAY in a sentence: ....

....

What's good about my life: ....

....

What I did well today: ....

....

Blah: ....

....

MOODS

HABITS

WEDNESDAY in a sentence: ....

....

What's good about my life: ....

....

What I did well today: ....

....

Blah: ....

....

MOODS

HABITS

THURSDAY in a sentence: ....

....

What's good about my life: ....

....

What I did well today: ....

....

Blah: ....

....

MOODS

HABITS

FRIDAY in a sentence: ....

What's good about my life: ....

What I did well today: ....

Blah: ....

MOODS

HABITS

SATURDAY in a sentence: ....

What's good about my life: ....

What I did well today: ....

Blah: ....

MOODS

HABITS

SUNDAY in a sentence: ....

What's good about my life: ....

What I did well today: ....

Blah: ....

MOODS

HABITS

Week In Review: ....

YA WIN SOME, YA LOSE SOME
The best & worst of this week

YAY!

BOO!

RATE THIS WEEK'S
OVERALL HAPPYISHNESS:

UN-HAPPYISH   HAPPYISH

Week Of:

MONDAY in a sentence:
....

What's good about my life: ....

What I did well today: ....

Blah: ....

MOODS ○ ○ ○ ○

HABITS ○ ○ ○ ○

TUESDAY in a sentence: ....
....

What's good about my life: ....

What I did well today: ....

Blah: ....

MOODS ○ ○ ○ ○

HABITS ○ ○ ○ ○

WEDNESDAY in a sentence: ....

What's good about my life: ....

What I did well today: ....

Blah: ....

MOODS ○ ○ ○ ○

HABITS ○ ○ ○ ○

THURSDAY in a sentence: ....

What's good about my life: ....

What I did well today: ....

Blah: ....

MOODS ○ ○ ○ ○

HABITS ○ ○ ○ ○

FRIDAY in a sentence: ....

....

What's good about my life: ....

What I did well today: ....

Blah: ....

MOODS ○ ○ ○ ○

HABITS ○ ○ ○ ○

SATURDAY in a sentence: ....

What's good about my life: ....

What I did well today: ....

Blah: ....

MOODS ○ ○ ○ ○

HABITS ○ ○ ○ ○

SUNDAY in a sentence: ....

What's good about my life: ....

What I did well today: ....

Blah: ....

MOODS ○ ○ ○ ○

HABITS ○ ○ ○ ○

Week In Review: ....

YA WIN SOME, YA LOSE SOME
The best & worst of this week

YAY!

BOO!

RATE THIS WEEK'S
OVERALL HAPPYISHNESS:

UN-HAPPYISH   HAPPYISH

Month In Review:

QUIT LIST: What are the things/people/actions/thoughts you can quit this month: the weekly yoga class you dread? The coffee shop with the rude baristas? Your morning doomscroll? These are tangible changes you can make... but you don't have to!

I quit... ....

....

....

....

BRAGGABLE: Please save your humble pie for another occasion. This is a space to tell yourself everything you did well this month. Like, everything. You flossed once? You didn't roll your eyes at your annoying neighbor? You told your partner exactly why you were angry instead of making them guess? WELL DONE!

I feel great about... ....

....

....

....

LET IT BURN: Let's not pretend that everything is perfect or fine or just dandy. Here's a space for you to write down all your icky stuff: the jealous feelings that make you feel gross, the negative things you say to yourself, the texts you wanted to send but didn't, because you knew it was totally inappropriate. Write it down. Tear it out. Burn it up. Or just fold the page over. The point is... these are the things you can let go.

I acknowledge & let go of... ....

....

....

....

YOU ARE NOT A SAD STORY.

Week Of:

MONDAY in a sentence: ....

....

What's good about my life: ....

What I did well today: ....

....

Blah: ....

MOODS

HABITS

TUESDAY in a sentence: ....

....

What's good about my life: ....

What I did well today: ....

....

Blah: ....

MOODS

HABITS

WEDNESDAY in a sentence: ....

....

What's good about my life: ....

What I did well today: ....

....

Blah: ....

MOODS

HABITS

THURSDAY in a sentence: ....

What's good about my life: ....

What I did well today: ....

....

Blah: ....

MOODS

HABITS

FRIDAY in a sentence: ....

MOODS

What's good about my life: ....

What I did well today: ....

HABITS

Blah: ....

SATURDAY in a sentence: ....

MOODS

What's good about my life: ....

What I did well today: ....

HABITS

Blah: ....

SUNDAY in a sentence: ....

MOODS

What's good about my life: ....

What I did well today: ....

HABITS

Blah: ....

Week In Review: ....

YA WIN SOME, YA LOSE SOME
The best & worst of this week

YAY!   BOO!

RATE THIS WEEK'S
OVERALL HAPPYISHNESS:

UN-HAPPYISH   HAPPYISH

Week Of:

MONDAY in a sentence: ....

....

What's good about my life: ....

....

What I did well today: ....

....

Blah: ....

....

MOODS

HABITS

TUESDAY in a sentence: ....

....

What's good about my life: ....

....

What I did well today: ....

....

Blah: ....

....

MOODS

HABITS

WEDNESDAY in a sentence: ....

....

What's good about my life: ....

....

What I did well today: ....

....

Blah: ....

....

MOODS

HABITS

THURSDAY in a sentence: ....

....

What's good about my life: ....

....

What I did well today: ....

....

Blah: ....

....

MOODS

HABITS

FRIDAY in a sentence: ....

....

What's good about my life: ....

What I did well today: ....

Blah: ....

....

MOODS ○ ○ ○ ○

HABITS ○ ○ ○ ○

SATURDAY in a sentence: ....

....

What's good about my life ....

What I did well today: ....

Blah: ....

....

MOODS ○ ○ ○ ○

HABITS ○ ○ ○ ○

SUNDAY in a sentence: ....

....

What's good about my life: ....

What I did well today: ....

Blah: ....

....

MOODS ○ ○ ○ ○

HABITS ○ ○ ○ ○

Week In Review: ....

YA WIN SOME, YA LOSE SOME
The best & worst of this week

YAY!

BOO!

RATE THIS WEEK'S
OVERALL HAPPYISHNESS:

UN-HAPPYISH   HAPPYISH

Week Of:

MONDAY in a sentence: ....

....

What's good about my life: ....

What I did well today: ....

Blah: ....

MOODS ○ ○ ○ ○

HABITS ○ ○ ○ ○

TUESDAY in a sentence: ....

....

What's good about my life: ....

What I did well today: ....

Blah: ....

MOODS ○ ○ ○ ○

HABITS ○ ○ ○ ○

WEDNESDAY in a sentence: ....

....

What's good about my life: ....

What I did well today: ....

Blah: ....

MOODS ○ ○ ○ ○

HABITS ○ ○ ○ ○

THURSDAY in a sentence: ....

What's good about my life: ....

What I did well today: ....

Blah: ....

MOODS ○ ○ ○ ○

HABITS ○ ○ ○ ○

FRIDAY in a sentence: ....

....

What's good about my life: ....

....

What I did well today: ....

....

Blah: ....

....

MOODS

HABITS

SATURDAY in a sentence: ....

....

What's good about my life: ....

....

What I did well today: ....

....

Blah: ....

....

MOODS

HABITS

SUNDAY in a sentence: ....

....

What's good about my life: ....

....

What I did well today: ....

....

Blah: ....

....

MOODS

HABITS

Week In Review: ....

YA WIN SOME, YA LOSE SOME
The best & worst of this week

YAY!

BOO!

RATE THIS WEEK'S
OVERALL HAPPYISHNESS:

UN-HAPPYISH   HAPPYISH

Week Of:

MONDAY in a sentence:..

....

What's good about my life: ....

....

What I did well today: ....

....

Blah: ....

....

MOODS

HABITS

TUESDAY in a sentence:..

....

What's good about my life: ....

....

What I did well today: ....

....

Blah: ....

....

MOODS

HABITS

WEDNESDAY in a sentence: ....

....

What's good about my life: ....

....

What I did well today: ....

....

Blah: ....

....

MOODS

HABITS

THURSDAY in a sentence: ....

....

What's good about my life: ....

....

What I did well today: ....

....

Blah: ....

....

MOODS

HABITS

FRIDAY in a sentence: ....

....

What's good about my life: ....

....

What I did well today: ....

....

Blah: ....

....

MOODS ○ ○ ○ ○

HABITS ○ ○ ○ ○

SATURDAY in a sentence: ....

....

What's good about my life: ....

....

What I did well today: ....

....

Blah: ....

....

MOODS ○ ○ ○ ○

HABITS ○ ○ ○ ○

SUNDAY in a sentence: ....

....

What's good about my life: ....

....

What I did well today: ....

....

Blah: ....

....

MOODS ○ ○ ○ ○

HABITS ○ ○ ○ ○

Week In Review: ....

YA WIN SOME, YA LOSE SOME
The best & worst of this week

YAY!

BOO!

RATE THIS WEEK'S
OVERALL HAPPYISHNESS:

UN-HAPPYISH   HAPPYISH

QUIT LIST: What are the things/people/actions/thoughts you can quit this month: the weekly yoga class you dread? The coffee shop with the rude baristas? Your morning doomscroll? These are tangible changes you can make... but you don't have to!

I quit... ....

....

....

....

BRAGGABLE: Please save your humble pie for another occasion. This is a space to tell yourself everything you did well this month. Like, everything. You flossed once? You didn't roll your eyes at your annoying neighbor? You told your partner exactly why you were angry instead of making them guess? WELL DONE!

I feel great about... ....

....

....

....

LET IT BURN: Let's not pretend that everything is perfect or fine or just dandy. Here's a space for you to write down all your icky stuff: the jealous feelings that make you feel gross, the negative things you say to yourself, the texts you wanted to send but didn't, because you knew it was totally inappropriate. Write it down. Tear it out. Burn it up. Or just fold the page over. The point is... these are the things you can let go.

I acknowledge & let go of... ....

....

....

....

....

Teddy Roosevelt said,

"COMPARISON IS THE THIEF OF JOY."

He was right. Keep your eyes on your own paper—there's no competition for "best adult."

Week Of:

MONDAY in a sentence: ....
....

What's good about my life: ....
....

What I did well today: ....
....

Blah: ....
....

MOODS

HABITS

TUESDAY in a sentence: ....
....

What's good about my life: ....
....

What I did well today: ....
....

Blah: ....
....

MOODS

HABITS

WEDNESDAY in a sentence: ....
....

What's good about my life: ....
....

What I did well today: ....
....

Blah: ....
....

MOODS

HABITS

THURSDAY in a sentence: ....
....

What's good about my life: ....
....

What I did well today: ....
....

Blah: ....
....

MOODS

HABITS

FRIDAY in a sentence: ....

....

What's good about my life: ....

....

What I did well today: ....

....

Blah: ....

....

MOODS

HABITS

SATURDAY in a sentence: ....

....

What's good about my life: ....

....

What I did well today: ....

....

Blah: ....

....

MOODS

HABITS

SUNDAY in a sentence: ....

....

What's good about my life: ....

....

What I did well today: ....

....

Blah: ....

....

MOODS

HABITS

Week In Review: ....

YA WIN SOME, YA LOSE SOME
The best & worst of this week

YAY!

BOO!

RATE THIS WEEK'S
OVERALL HAPPYISHNESS:

UN-HAPPYISH   HAPPYISH

Week Of:

MONDAY in a sentence: ....

....

What's good about my life: ....

....

What I did well today: ....

....

Blah: ....

MOODS

HABITS

TUESDAY in a sentence: ....

....

What's good about my life: ....

....

What I did well today: ....

....

Blah: ....

MOODS

HABITS

WEDNESDAY in a sentence: ....

....

What's good about my life: ....

....

What I did well today: ....

....

Blah: ....

MOODS

HABITS

THURSDAY in a sentence: ....

....

What's good about my life: ....

....

What I did well today: ....

....

Blah: ....

MOODS

HABITS

FRIDAY in a sentence: ....

....

What's good about my life: ....

....

What I did well today: ....

....

Blah: ....

MOODS

HABITS

SATURDAY in a sentence: ....

....

What's good about my life: ....

....

What I did well today: ....

....

Blah: ....

MOODS

HABITS

SUNDAY in a sentence: ....

....

What's good about my life: ....

....

What I did well today: ....

....

Blah: ....

MOODS

HABITS

Week In Review: ....

YA WIN SOME, YA LOSE SOME
The best & worst of this week

YAY!

BOO!

RATE THIS WEEK'S
OVERALL HAPPYISHNESS:

UN-HAPPYISH   HAPPYISH

Week Of:

MONDAY in a sentence:...

What's good about my life:..

What I did well today:..

Blah:..

MOODS

HABITS

TUESDAY in a sentence:..

What's good about my life:..

What I did well today:..

Blah:..

MOODS

HABITS

WEDNESDAY in a sentence:...

What's good about my life:..

What I did well today:..

Blah:..

MOODS

HABITS

THURSDAY in a sentence:..

What's good about my life:..

What I did well today:..

Blah:..

MOODS

HABITS

FRIDAY in a sentence: ....

....

What's good about my life: ....

....

What I did well today: ....

....

Blah: ....

....

MOODS ○ ○ ○ ○

HABITS ○ ○ ○ ○

SATURDAY in a sentence: ....

....

What's good about my life: ....

....

What I did well today: ....

....

Blah: ....

....

MOODS ○ ○ ○ ○

HABITS ○ ○ ○ ○

SUNDAY in a sentence: ....

....

What's good about my life: ....

....

What I did well today: ....

....

Blah: ....

....

MOODS ○ ○ ○ ○

HABITS ○ ○ ○ ○

Week In Review: ....

YA WIN SOME, YA LOSE SOME
The best & worst of this week

YAY!

BOO!

RATE THIS WEEK'S
OVERALL HAPPYISHNESS:

UN-HAPPYISH   HAPPYISH

Week Of:

MONDAY in a sentence:...

What's good about my life:...

What I did well today:...

Blah:...

MOODS

HABITS

TUESDAY in a sentence:...

What's good about my life:...

What I did well today:...

Blah:...

MOODS

HABITS

WEDNESDAY in a sentence:...

What's good about my life:...

What I did well today:...

Blah:...

MOODS

HABITS

THURSDAY in a sentence:...

What's good about my life:...

What I did well today:...

Blah:...

MOODS

HABITS

FRIDAY in a sentence: ....

What's good about my life: ....

What I did well today: ....

Blah: ....

MOODS ○ ○ ○ ○

HABITS ○ ○ ○ ○

SATURDAY in a sentence: ....

What's good about my life: ....

What I did well today: ....

Blah: ....

MOODS ○ ○ ○ ○

HABITS ○ ○ ○ ○

SUNDAY in a sentence: ....

What's good about my life: ....

What I did well today: ....

Blah: ....

MOODS ○ ○ ○ ○

HABITS ○ ○ ○ ○

Week In Review: ....

YA WIN SOME, YA LOSE SOME
The best & worst of this week

YAY!

BOO!

RATE THIS WEEK'S
OVERALL HAPPYISHNESS:

UN-HAPPYISH   HAPPYISH

Month In Review:

QUIT LIST: What are the things/people/actions/thoughts you can quit this month: the weekly yoga class you dread? The coffee shop with the rude baristas? Your morning doomscroll? These are tangible changes you can make... but you don't have to!

I quit... ....

....

....

....

....

BRAGGABLE: Please save your humble pie for another occasion. This is a space to tell yourself everything you did well this month. Like, everything. You flossed once? You didn't roll your eyes at your annoying neighbor? You told your partner exactly why you were angry instead of making them guess? WELL DONE!

I feel great about... ....

....

....

....

....

LET IT BURN: Let's not pretend that everything is perfect or fine or just dandy. Here's a space for you to write down all your icky stuff: the jealous feelings that make you feel gross, the negative things you say to yourself, the texts you wanted to send but didn't, because you knew it was totally inappropriate. Write it down. Tear it out. Burn it up. Or just fold the page over. The point is... these are the things you can let go.

I acknowledge & let go of... ....

....

....

....

....

PERFECTION IS A LIE

perpetuated by boring people.
Seriously, have you ever met an
interesting perfect person?
I didn't think so.

Week Of:

MONDAY in a sentence: ....

....

What's good about my life: ....

What I did well today: ....

Blah: ....

MOODS

HABITS

TUESDAY in a sentence: ....

....

What's good about my life: ....

What I did well today: ....

Blah: ....

MOODS

HABITS

WEDNESDAY in a sentence: ....

....

What's good about my life: ....

What I did well today: ....

Blah: ....

MOODS

HABITS

THURSDAY in a sentence: ....

What's good about my life: ....

What I did well today: ....

Blah: ....

MOODS

HABITS

FRIDAY in a sentence: ....

....

What's good about my life: ....

....

What I did well today: ....

....

Blah: ....

....

MOODS ○ ○ ○ ○

HABITS ○ ○ ○ ○

SATURDAY in a sentence: ....

....

What's good about my life: ....

....

What I did well today: ....

....

Blah: ....

....

MOODS ○ ○ ○ ○

HABITS ○ ○ ○ ○

SUNDAY in a sentence: ....

....

What's good about my life: ....

....

What I did well today: ....

....

Blah: ....

....

MOODS ○ ○ ○ ○

HABITS ○ ○ ○ ○

Week In Review: ....

YA WIN SOME, YA LOSE SOME
The best & worst of this week

YAY!

BOO!

RATE THIS WEEK'S
OVERALL HAPPYISHNESS:

UN-HAPPYISH   HAPPYISH

Week Of:

MONDAY in a sentence:..

....

What's good about my life:..

....

What I did well today:..

....

Blah:..

....

MOODS

HABITS

TUESDAY in a sentence:..

....

What's good about my life:..

....

What I did well today:..

....

Blah:..

....

MOODS

HABITS

WEDNESDAY in a sentence:..

....

What's good about my life:..

....

What I did well today:..

....

Blah:..

....

MOODS

HABITS

THURSDAY in a sentence:..

....

What's good about my life:..

What I did well today:..

....

Blah:..

....

MOODS

HABITS

FRIDAY in a sentence: ....

....

What's good about my life: ....

....

What I did well today: ....

....

Blah: ....

....

MOODS

○ ○ ○ ○

HABITS

○ ○ ○ ○

SATURDAY in a sentence: ....

....

What's good about my life: ....

....

What I did well today: ....

....

Blah: ....

....

MOODS

○ ○ ○ ○

HABITS

○ ○ ○ ○

SUNDAY in a sentence: ....

....

What's good about my life: ....

....

What I did well today: ....

....

Blah: ....

....

MOODS

○ ○ ○ ○

HABITS

○ ○ ○ ○

Week In Review: ....

YA WIN SOME, YA LOSE SOME
The best & worst of this week

RATE THIS WEEK'S
OVERALL HAPPYISHNESS:

YAY!   BOO!

UN-HAPPYISH   HAPPYISH

Week Of:

MONDAY in a sentence:..

....

What's good about my life:..

....

What I did well today:..

....

Blah:...

....

MOODS ○ ○ ○ ○

HABITS ○ ○ ○ ○

TUESDAY in a sentence:..

....

What's good about my life:..

....

What I did well today:..

....

Blah:...

....

MOODS ○ ○ ○ ○

HABITS ○ ○ ○ ○

WEDNESDAY in a sentence:.......................................

....

What's good about my life:..

....

What I did well today:..

....

Blah:...

....

MOODS ○ ○ ○ ○

HABITS ○ ○ ○ ○

THURSDAY in a sentence:...

....

What's good about my life:..

....

What I did well today:..

....

Blah:...

....

MOODS ○ ○ ○ ○

HABITS ○ ○ ○ ○

FRIDAY in a sentence: ....

....

What's good about my life: ....

....

What I did well today: ....

....

Blah: ....

....

MOODS

HABITS

SATURDAY in a sentence: ....

....

What's good about my life: ....

....

What I did well today: ....

....

Blah: ....

....

MOODS

HABITS

SUNDAY in a sentence: ....

....

What's good about my life: ....

....

What I did well today: ....

....

Blah: ....

....

MOODS

HABITS

Week In Review: ....

YA WIN SOME, YA LOSE SOME
The best & worst of this week

YAY!

BOO!

**RATE THIS WEEK'S
OVERALL HAPPYISHNESS:**

UN-HAPPYISH   HAPPYISH

Week Of:

MONDAY in a sentence: ....

....

What's good about my life: ....

....

What I did well today: ....

....

Blah: ....

MOODS ○ ○ ○ ○

HABITS ○ ○ ○ ○

TUESDAY in a sentence: ....

....

What's good about my life: ....

....

What I did well today: ....

....

Blah: ....

....

MOODS ○ ○ ○ ○

HABITS ○ ○ ○ ○

WEDNESDAY in a sentence: ....

....

What's good about my life: ....

....

What I did well today: ....

....

Blah: ....

....

MOODS ○ ○ ○ ○

HABITS ○ ○ ○ ○

THURSDAY in a sentence: ....

....

What's good about my life: ....

....

What I did well today: ....

....

Blah: ....

....

MOODS ○ ○ ○ ○

HABITS ○ ○ ○ ○

FRIDAY in a sentence: ....

....

What's good about my life: ....

....

What I did well today: ....

....

Blah: ....

....

MOODS ○ ○ ○ ○

HABITS ○ ○ ○ ○

SATURDAY in a sentence: ....

....

What's good about my life: ....

....

What I did well today: ....

....

Blah: ....

....

MOODS ○ ○ ○ ○

HABITS ○ ○ ○ ○

SUNDAY in a sentence: ....

....

What's good about my life: ....

....

What I did well today: ....

....

Blah: ....

....

MOODS ○ ○ ○ ○

HABITS ○ ○ ○ ○

Week In Review: ....

YA WIN SOME, YA LOSE SOME
The best & worst of this week

YAY!

BOO!

RATE THIS WEEK'S OVERALL HAPPYISHNESS:

UN-HAPPYISH   HAPPYISH

Month In Review:

QUIT LIST: What are the things/people/actions/thoughts you can quit this month: the weekly yoga class you dread? The coffee shop with the rude baristas? Your morning doomscroll? These are tangible changes you can make... but you don't have to!

I quit... ....

....

....

....

....

BRAGGABLE: Please save your humble pie for another occasion. This is a space to tell yourself everything you did well this month. Like, everything. You flossed once? You didn't roll your eyes at your annoying neighbor? You told your partner exactly why you were angry instead of making them guess? WELL DONE!

I feel great about... ....

....

....

....

....

LET IT BURN: Let's not pretend that everything is perfect or fine or just dandy. Here's a space for you to write down all your icky stuff: the jealous feelings that make you feel gross, the negative things you say to yourself, the texts you wanted to send but didn't, because you knew it was totally inappropriate. Write it down. Tear it out. Burn it up. Or just fold the page over. The point is... these are the things you can let go.

I acknowledge & let go of... ....

....

....

....

....

THESE ARE THE DIAMONDS

I picked from the darkness,
that shine with meaning
only for me.

WOOHOO!

You did it! You reached the end of this journal. Well, almost. We don't have a ceremony or a certificate, but one of my favorite parts of ending a journal is looking back at it to see what kind of year I really had. Because time moves fast and I tend to think of my most recent feeling as the truest one, even though I know in my brain that a bad day does not equal a bad year! I know what they say about assuming, but I'm still going to assume that if you were the kind of person to pick up a journal with this title, you are probably a person who has gone through or is going through some stuff. I hope these pages have offered you a way to document without judgment, space to reflect without rumination, and the reassurance that even when things are crappy, you're doing a good job.

I'm proud of you, stranger, and I wish you endless happyishness in the days to come.

XO,

Nora

Year In Review:

OK, now just one final thing! Take a few days to look it over and see the past 52 weeks through the eyes of your current self...

I'm proud of...

I'm embarrassed by...

I did a good job at...

The highlights of my year were... ....
....
....
....
....
....
....
....
....

The lowlights of my year were... ....
....
....
....
....
....
....
....
....

My overall happyishness was... ....
....
....
....
....
....
....
....
....

I WISH YOU A MILLION HAPPYISH DAYS AHEAD.

Nora